SING-ALONG WITH A LIVE *Jazz* BAND

WISE PUBLICATIONS
part of The Music Sales Group
London / New York / Paris / Sydney / Copenhagen / Berlin / Madrid / Hong Kong / Tokyo

Published by
WISE PUBLICATIONS
14-15 Berners Street, London W1T 3LJ, UK.

Exclusive Distributors:
MUSIC SALES LIMITED
Distribution Centre, Newmarket Road, Bury St Edmunds, Suffolk IP33 3YB, UK.
MUSIC SALES PTY LIMITED
20 Resolution Drive, Caringbah, NSW 2229, Australia.

Order No. AM998998
ISBN 978-1-84938-308-0
This book © Copyright 2010 Wise Publications,
a division of Music Sales Limited.

Compiled by Nick Crispin
Edited by Lizzie Moore
Music arranged by Paul Honey
Music processed by Paul Ewers Music Design
Song Background Notes by Michael Heatley
Cover design by Adela Casacuberta
Printed in the EU

CD recorded, mixed and mastered by Jonas Persson
Keyboard: Paul Honey
Bass: Phil Mulford
Drums: Chris Baron
Vocals: Ruth Searle and Jeff Shadley

FREE bonus material

Download band scores and parts to your computer.

Visit www.hybridpublications.com

Registration is free and easy.

Your registration code is: DJ972

Song Background Notes

Birdland
Weather Report

Weather Report, founded by the twin talents of ex-Miles Davis sidemen Joe Zawinul (keyboards) and Wayne Shorter (saxophone), dominated the modern jazz scene in the 1970s. This funky instrumental was penned by Zawinul and named after the New York jazz club on 52nd Street that itself pays homage to saxophonist Charlie 'Bird' Parker. Taken from the album *Heavy Weather*, 'Birdland' became an unlikely US hit single in 1977 and a modern standard that entered the repertoire of bands ranging from Buddy Rich and Maynard Ferguson to The Manhattan Transfer, whose version featured lyrics by Jon Hendricks.

Desafinado (Slightly Out Of Tune)
Antonio Carlos Jobim

The bossa nova craze developed from samba in Brazil around 1958. It arrived in the US in 1962 via American jazz musician Charlie Byrd who had heard the music of Antonio Carlos Jobim and others while touring in South America. Byrd's collaborator, saxophonist Stan Getz, had a hit with an adaptation of Jobim's 'One Note Samba' and then won a Grammy for Best Jazz Performance of 1963 with 'Desafinado', the English translation of which is 'Slightly Out Of Tune' or 'Off Key'. Jobim moved to the US to capitalise on this, and his first album there was entitled *The Composer Of Desafinado, Plays*.

Feeling Good
Nina Simone

Nina Simone discovered and interpreted some memorable songs during a distinguished career that encompassed half a century. She found 'Feeling Good' in the 1965 musical *The Roar Of The Greasepaint – The Smell of The Crowd* and recorded it that very year. It finally made the UK chart in 1994, nine years before her passing, thanks to its use in the movie *Point Of No Return*. It's her impassioned version that Michael Bublé, John Barrowman, George Michael and others have used as their reference point, but credit is also due to writers Anthony Newley and Leslie Bricusse for the joyous combination of words and music that started the ball rolling.

Fever
Eva Cassidy

Though the world only caught up with the brilliance of US songbird Eva Cassidy after her death in 1996, the recordings she left behind have allowed millions to enjoy her timeless talent. 'Fever' was first recorded in the fifties by bluesman Little Willie John but became associated with Peggy Lee after she rewrote the first two verses and supplied a new arrangement in 1958. Elvis Presley recorded a near-identical version to Lee's Number 8 hit for his album *Elvis Is Back!* and a standard was born. But Eva recorded it as was originally intended when written by Eddie Cooley and John Davenport (Otis Blackwell) in 1956. Her brother Dan added violin to a first-take vocal, and the result is both spellbinding and spine-chilling.

Fly Me To The Moon (In Other Words)
Julie London

Sultry Julie London's impact was such that she was voted one of the world's top female vocalists of 1955, 1956 and 1957, yet like Frank Sinatra she continued a parallel acting career. This song was written in 1954 by Bart Howard as 'In Other Words', and, though it soon became known as 'Fly Me To The Moon' from its first line, it took a few years for the publishers to change the title. Sinatra's version from 1964's *It Might As Well Be Swing* collaboration with Count Basie may be the best known, but Julie's husky rendition has been adopted by a new generation thanks to its appearance in *Bridget Jones' Diary*.

Let's Get Lost
Chet Baker

Though legendary singer-trumpeter Chet Baker died in 1988, his music was the toast of Hollywood as a new millennium began, thanks to *The Talented Mr Ripley*. The film's five Oscar nominations included Best Original Score, director Anthony Minghella having put Baker's music at the heart of the film. A more direct screen tribute, a documentary shot the year of his death and directed by Bruce Weber, took 'Let's Get Lost' as its title. It was nominated for an Oscar but played up to the image of Baker as a wasted talent. Within its dreamy, romantic lyric, 'Let's Get Lost' rivals 'My Funny Valentine' as Baker's best-known song.

Take Five
Dave Brubeck

One of the most popular jazz musicians of the last century, keyboardist and bandleader Dave Brubeck arguably did more to promote modern jazz than any other player. His alto saxophonist Paul Desmond wrote 'Take Five', the first and biggest of a series of pop hits for Brubeck's Quartet that brought the concept of modern jazz to a whole new generation in 1960-61. Brubeck experimented with time signatures through much of his career ('Take Five' is in 5/4 time), while Desmond, who died in 1977, left all future royalties from the jazz classic he penned to the American Red Cross.

Take The 'A' Train
Duke Ellington

Acknowledged as unquestionably one of the finest composers to have emerged from 20th-century America, Edward Kennedy 'Duke' Ellington painted many memorable sound pictures during half a century of music-making. 'Take The 'A' Train' was penned by young pianist and composer Billy Strayhorn who, in 1939, travelled from his Pittsburgh home to New York hoping to meet the Duke. He brought a composition he'd written using the travel instructions Ellington's office had given him to get to the band's venue that night. The tune was played to Duke who liked it enough to take Strayhorn onto his payroll.

Well You Needn't
Jamie Cullum

British pianist-singer Jamie Cullum dragged jazz kicking and screaming into the new millennium after making waves with his debut album in 1999. The Thelonious Monk classic 'Well You Needn't' received a refreshing new arrangement on second album, *Pointless Nostalgic*, where it nestled next to Radiohead's similarly re-interpreted 'High And Dry'. 'Well You Needn't' caught the ear of veteran broadcaster Michael Parkinson - who may well have remembered the original from 1944, to which Mike Ferro added lyrics in the seventies - and fame for Jamie was just around the corner. Indeed, he has since been certified the UK's biggest-selling jazz artist of all time.

When The Saints Go Marching In
Louis Armstrong

'Saints' is a typical African-American spiritual with its roots in the days of slavery. It would have stayed in church had it not been for Louis Armstrong who, when traditional New Orleans jazz enjoyed a revival in the 1930s, turned to the New Orleans music tradition for material. Armstrong's first recording of 'Saints' in May 1938 saw him set up a mock 'jazz church' for the occasion, with himself as the preacher. He scrapped everything except the first verse and used his unique sense of phrasing on the lyric. 'Sachmo' would go on to record more than 40 versions of a song now identified with him.

Duke Ellington

Dave Brubeck

Chet Baker

Antonio Carlos Jobim

Louis Armstrong

Birdland

Words by Jon Hendricks
Music by Josef Zawinul

Demo track: Track 01
Backing track: Track 11

Desafinado
(Slightly Out Of Tune)

Words & Music by Newton Mendonca & Antonio Carlos Jobim
English Words by Jon Hendricks & Jessie Cavanaugh

Demo track: Track 02
Backing track: Track 12

Moderate Bossa Nova

2 BAR COUNT-IN.

If you say my singing is off key, my love. You will hurt my feel-ings, don't you see my love? I wish I had an ear like yours, a voice that would be-have. All I have is feel-ing and the voice God gave. You in-sist my mu-sic goes a-gainst the rules. Yes, but rules were nev-er made for love-sick fools. I wrote this lit-tle song for you, but you don't care. It's a crook-ed song, ah, but all my heart is there. The things that you would see if you would do your part, is e-ven if I'm out of tune, I have a gen-tle heart. I took your pic-ture with my trus-ty Rol-lei-flex, and now all I have de-vel-oped is a com-plex.

Feeling Good

Words & Music by Leslie Bricusse & Anthony Newley

Demo track: Track 03
Backing track: Track 13

But-ter-flies all hav - in' fun,___ you know what I mean. Sleep in peace when day___ is

done_that's what I mean. In this old world, in this new world___ and a bold world___ for___

me.___

Stars___ when you shine,___ you know how I feel.___ Scent of the pine___ you

know how_ I feel. Oh, free-dom___ is___ mine___ and I know how I feel.___ It's a

new dawn,_ it's a new day,_ it's a new life___ for___ me, and I'm feel - in'

good, and I'm feel - in' good, you know how I feel. It's a

new dawn,_ it's a new day,_ it's a new life___ for___ me, and I'm feel - in' good.

Fly Me To The Moon
(In Other Words)

Demo track: Track 04
Backing track: Track 14

Words & Music by Bart Howard

Let's Get Lost

Words by Frank Loesser
Music by Jimmy McHugh

Demo track: Track 05
Backing track: Track 15

Let's ___ get lost, ___ let them send out a - larms.

And though they'll think us ra - ther rude, ___

let's tell the world we're in that cra - zy mood.

Let's ___ de - frost ___ in a ro - man - tic mist.

Let's ___ get crossed, ___ crossed off ev - 'ry - bod - y's list.

To cel - e - brate this night we found each oth - er,

D.S. al Coda

mm, ___ let's get lost.

37

𝄋 *Coda*

Mm, ___ let's get, oh, ___ let's get, mm, ___ let's get lost.

Fever

Words & Music by John Davenport & Eddie Cooley

Demo track: Track 06
Backing track: Track 16

Moderate swing ♩ = 134

Take Five

Music by Paul Desmond
Words by Dave Brubeck & Iola Brubeck

Demo track: Track 07
Backing track: Track 17

Won't you stop and take a lit-tle time out with me just take five, just take five. Just stop your cra-zy day and take the time out to see that I'm a-live I'm a-live. Al-though I'm go-ing out of my way, just so I can pass by each day, not a sin-gle word do we say, it's a pan-to-mime and not a play. Still I know our eyes of-ten meet, I feel tin-gles down to my feet, when you smile that's much too dis-creet you send me on my way. Now would-n't it be

take a lit-tle time out with me,___ Now ba-by take five. Just stop your bus-y

day and take the time out to see girl, that I'm a - live. Though I'm go-ing

out of my way, just so I can pass by each day, not a sin-gle word do we say, it's a pan-to-

-mime and not a play. Still I know our eyes of - ten meet, I feel tin - gles

down to my feet, when you smile that's much too dis-creet you send-'in me on my way. Won't you stop and

take a lit-tle time out with me just take five, just_ take five. Just stop your cra-zy

day and take the time out to see that I'm___ a - live, I'm___ a - live.

That I'm a - live, I'm a - live,

I'm a - live, I'm a - live.___

Take The 'A' Train

Words & Music by Billy Strayhorn

Demo track: Track 08
Backing track: Track 18

'Straight ahead' moderate swing

♩ = 172

NO COUNT-IN

You_____ must take the A____ Train_____

to go to Sug-ar Hill way up in Har-lem._ If_____ you miss the A_

__ Train_____ you'll find you missed the quick-est way to Har-lem._

Hur-ry,_____ get on now it's com - ing._____

List-en_____ to_____ those rails a - thrum - ming._____ Oh_____

__ boy,_____ Get on the A_____ Train,_____

soon you will be in Sug-ar Hill in Har-lem. Ba

de-d'n doot-'n doot du boo-d'n day-yo doot-'n doot-'n doot-'n dey doot-'n doot-'n doot-'n doo-day-yah.__

Bob-'n doo-dey yid-dup ba - ha._____ Do-dey doot-'n doot-'n dee, day-yah._____ Be-bey

Well You Needn't

Words by Mike Ferro
Music by Thelonious Monk

Demo track: Track 09
Backing track: Track 19

ought-ta know you lost the glow, the beat is slow, the sha-dows grow the lights are low, it's time to go and

slow the show down. You're tak - in' off weight well you need - n't, you're

look - in' just great___ well you need - n't, you're set - tin' the bait___ well you

need - n't it's o - ver now, it's o - ver now.

Latin feel

Talk - in' so sweet well you need - n't, you

say you won't cheat well you need - n't, you're tap - pin' your feet___ well you need - n't, it's

o - ver now,___ it's o - ver now. You're dress - in' with class well you need - n't, you're

When The Saints Go Marching In

Traditional

Demo track: Track 10
Backing track: Track 20

Bright march tempo (swung ♪'s) ♩ = 96

CD Track Listing

To remove your CD from the plastic sleeve,
lift the small lip to break the perforations.
Replace the disc after use for convenient storage.